Map Reading Puz

GW00360384

by Jenny Alexander

Contents

Longman

Edinburgh Gate
Harlow, Essex

"Where's My New CD?"

"Where's my new CD?"

"I don't know! Let go of me!"

You can hear the argument from half way down the road. It's your friend Leah and her little brother. You are on the way to listen to Leah's new CD, so things are not looking good for you. Leah has her little brother in a neck hold, so things are not looking good for him, either.

Leah's little brother is either too brave or too stupid to tell her where he has hidden her CD. If you can find it, you might just save his life! Look at the plan of Leah's garden. Follow the directions to find out where the CD is hidden.

1 Start at the gate.

2 Go to the birdbath and take one step east from there.

3 Turn to the north and take 12 steps.

4 Turn to the east and take two and a half steps.

5 Take six steps north.

6 Take two steps east.

Where have you ended up?

To double check your answer, go to page 4. ▶

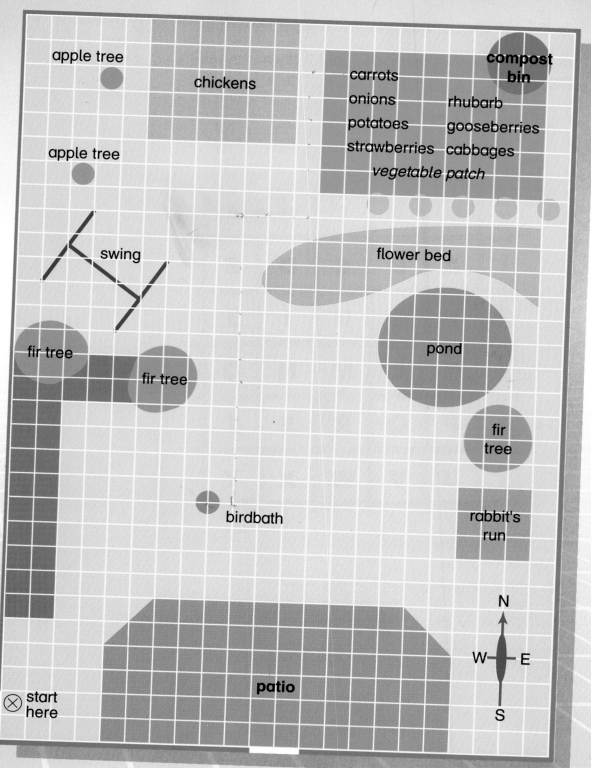

apple tree

chickens

carrots
onions
potatoes
strawberries

compost bin

rhubarb
gooseberries
cabbages

vegetable patch

apple tree

swing

flower bed

fir tree

fir tree

pond

fir tree

birdbath

rabbit's run

N

W — E

S

patio

⊗ start here

Scale: 1 square = one step

3

Use the alphabet grid to see if you were right about the CD.

You will need a pencil and paper. Jot down the letters you find in these squares:

2d   3d   4e   2c   1e

1c   1a   4c   4c   3e   4e   4d

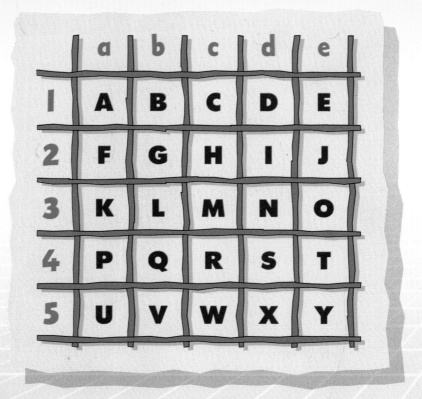

Is this where you ended up on the map?

Look on page 31 to check your answer. ▶

Running on Empty

Jan and Liz are driving along the M4 motorway on their way to visit friends in Malmesbury. They are coming up to **junction** 18, when Jan notices they have nearly run out of petrol. They have only enough left to go about 30 km.

Liz says they should leave the motorway and take a short cut on some minor roads. Jan says they should stay on the motorway.

Who is right?

Follow the instructions on page 6 to find out.

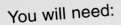

You will need:

● a ruler

● a pencil and paper

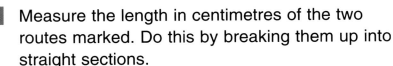

1 Measure the length in centimetres of the two routes marked. Do this by breaking them up into straight sections.

2 First measure Jan's route. Jot down the distances from A–B, B–C, C–D, D–E, E–F and F–G.

3 Add them together.

4 Now measure Liz's route. Jot down the distances from 1–2, 2–3, 3–4 and 4–5.

5 Add them together.

6 Now you know how many centimetres each route is on the map. Each centimetre represents 2 km. Multiply the number of centimetres by 2 to find out how many kilometres there are in each route.

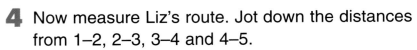

How far is Jan's route?

How far is Liz's route?

Look at page 8 to see if you were right. ▶

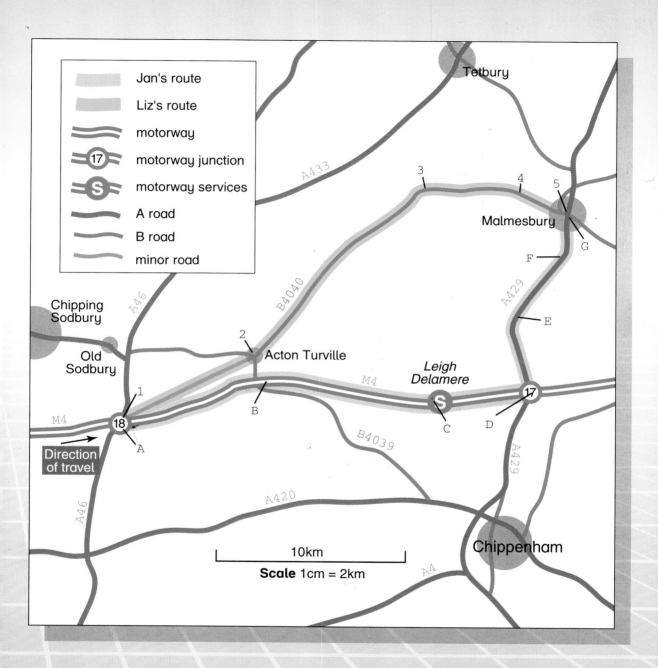

Tetbury

A433

3

4

5

Malmesbury

G

F

Chipping
Sodbury

A46

B4040

E

A429

Old
Sodbury

2

Acton Turville

Leigh
Delamere

M4

1

B

S

17

M4

18

C

D

Direction
of travel

A

A46

B4039

A429

A420

Chippenham

10km

A4

Scale 1cm = 2km

Legend

Jan's route

Liz's route

motorway

(17) motorway junction

(S) motorway services

A road

B road

minor road

Liz's route is 29 km, so they might just make it. Jan's route is 32 km, which is certainly too long. But Jan is right that they should stay on the motorway, because there are **services** at Leigh Delamere, so they can stop for petrol. There is no way of knowing from the map if they could get petrol on the minor roads.

Besides petrol, Jan wants to call in at the services for three other things. Find out what they are by looking in these squares:

G8   H6   F1

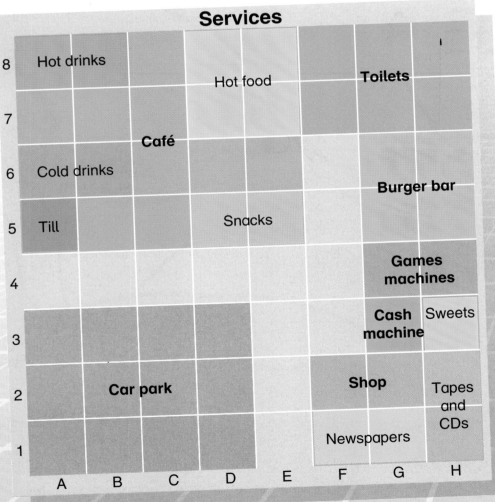

Services

	A	B	C	D	E	F	G	H
8	Hot drinks			Hot food			Toilets	
7								
6	Cold drinks		Café					Burger bar
5	Till			Snacks				
4							Games machines	
3							Cash machine	Sweets
2		Car park				Shop		Tapes and CDs
1						Newspapers		

Look on page 31 to see if you are right. ▶

The Disappearing Dinner

You are an alien from the planet Zura. You are visiting the planet Daak. You have had a wallow in the gloopswamp and now you are ready for dinner. But while you were in the gloopswamp, your dinner disappeared! Follow these instructions to see if you can find it.

Go between the nearest crater and the singing stones. Head towards the blooroot. When you get to him, go round him to the right. Mind you don't step on his roots. Go between the two baby blooroots. There is a crater in front of you. Look inside and you should find your dinner. Which crater is it? Read on to find out if you are right.

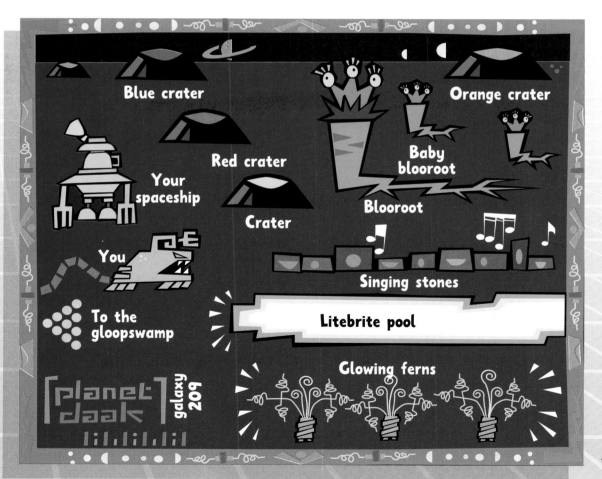

Your dinner has given you the slip again. If it's fast enough, it can get to the one place you will never find it. Where is that? Follow these instructions to find out.

1 Go back over the blooroot's roots. Mind you don't step on them!

2 Head straight for the singing stones.

3 Go over the singing stones and head towards the glowing ferns. (They glow in the Daak!)

4 Stop halfway there.

Where are you?

Look on page 31 to see where your dinner should hide. ▶

Dodgy Dave and Nina the Knife

This is Dodgy Dave. He is a small-time crook.

This is Nina the Knife. No – she isn't called "the Knife" for the reason you're thinking. She is called "the Knife" because of her terrible table manners!

Dave and Nina have just done a **burglary** in London. The police are after them. They try to give the police the slip, but as they are approaching Old Windsor – too fast – they crash their car on Albert Bridge. Nina hides under the bridge. Dave grabs the money and runs. When he is too tired to run any more, he dumps the bag full of money over a wall and goes back to look for Nina. It is not his lucky day. He gets run over by a cyclist!

Nina tracks Dave down in hospital. He tells her where he put the money. Does she find it? Could you? Follow Dave's directions and see. Start at Albert Bridge.

> **Go straight on past the pub until you come to a roundabout. Then take the road off to the right. It's a main road. Stay on it until it crosses a wide track.**
>
> **Turn left up the track. When you come to a choice of tracks, take the left fork. Keep going until you come to a lane. Turn left. That brings you onto a minor road. Go straight across. I threw the holdall over the wall.**

Where do you think the holdall is?

Turn to page 14 to see if you are right. ▶

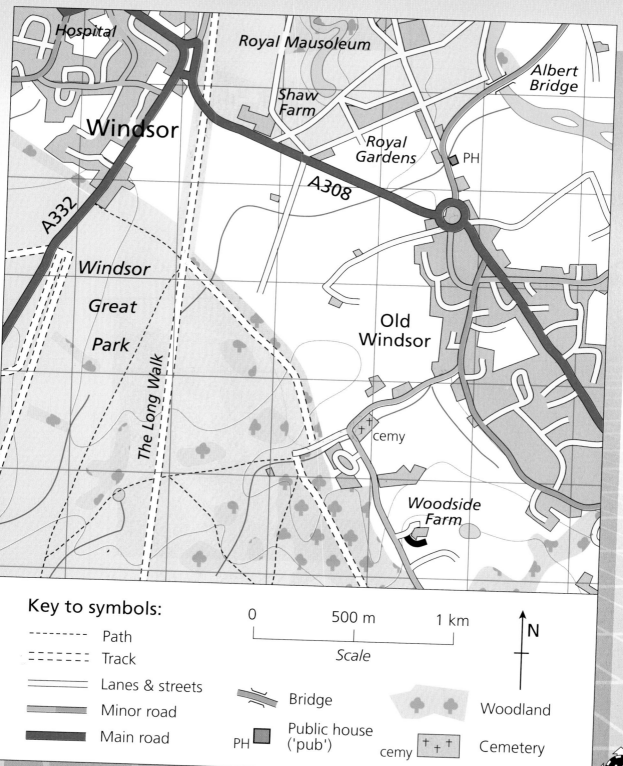

Key to symbols:

- - - - - - - - Path

- - - - - - Track

Lanes & streets

Minor road

Main road

Bridge

PH ▢ Public house ('pub')

Woodland

cemy ⊞ Cemetery

0   500 m   1 km
Scale

N

Hospital

Royal Mausoleum

Shaw Farm

Windsor

Royal Gardens

PH

Albert Bridge

A332

A308

Windsor Great Park

The Long Walk

Old Windsor

cemy

Woodside Farm

13

Nina Watson, known as Nina "the Knife" to her criminal friends, was caught today with a holdall full of stolen money. A man walking his dog raised the alarm when he saw someone behaving suspiciously in the **cemetery** in old Windsor.

Searching for Sweets

You are visiting Poshe Hall with your mum and dad, and you are feeling bored. You have seen a lot of boring old books in the library and study, and now you are looking at boring old plates in the dining room. To make matters worse, there are attendants in uniform all over the place, ready to jump on you if you touch anything.

Your dad has mercy on you and gives you some money to buy sweets in the gift shop. You ask the attendant how to get there.

Which door did you go through?

Turn to page 18 to see if you are in the right place. ▶

Poshe Hall

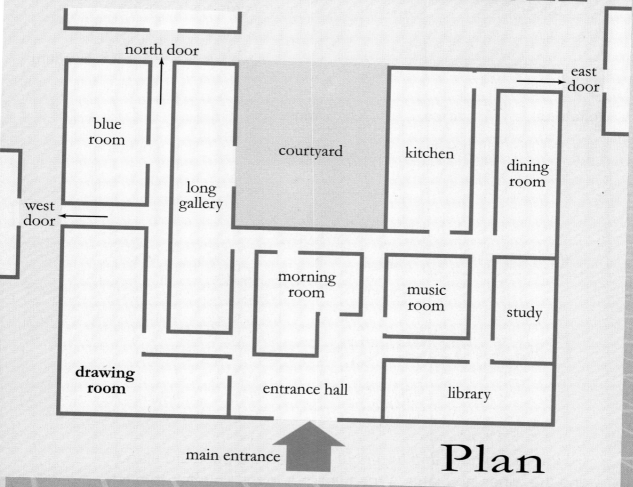

north door

east door

blue room

courtyard

kitchen

dining room

long gallery

west door

morning room

music room

study

drawing room

entrance hall

library

main entrance

Plan

If you went through the east door, you are in the car park!

If you went through the west door, you are in the queue for the toilets!

If you went through the north door, you have come to the gift shop.

You've found the gift shop, but where are the sweets?

Go inside the door and turn right between the postcard stand and the wines and jams. When you get to the counter, turn left. Turn right past the greetings cards, but stop before you reach the corner.

Are you looking in the right place? Check the answers on page 31 and see. ▶

The Newsman's Nose

Andy is training to be a **reporter** on his local newspaper. His boss says that to be a great reporter you have to learn to sniff out a good story. You have to develop what he calls "a newsman's nose".

But Andy doesn't see how he can sniff out a good story when all he gets to report on is boring village fêtes and weddings. Take this morning, for example. The boss has sent him to Balmoral, but not to interview a visiting royal or anything interesting like that. His job is to do an article on whisky making, and he has just done a tour of the **distillery**.

But as he comes out of the distillery he sees something that gets his newsman's nose twitching.

Could it be ...?

Andy whips out his camera and sets off on the trail of the mystery lady. If she's You Know Who, she will probably be going to the castle. But is she? Follow them and see.

Leaving the distillery, go left. Follow the road as it bears right through the woods. Go straight over the first crossroads. When you get to the **T-junction**, turn left. Go past the **obelisks**. When the road turns sharply to the right, follow it round. Go over the bridge, past the car park and up to the main road. Go right at the main road and, almost straight away, go left up a little lane. There is a building right in front of you.

Which building have Andy and the mystery lady reached?

Turn to page 22 to see if you are right. ▶

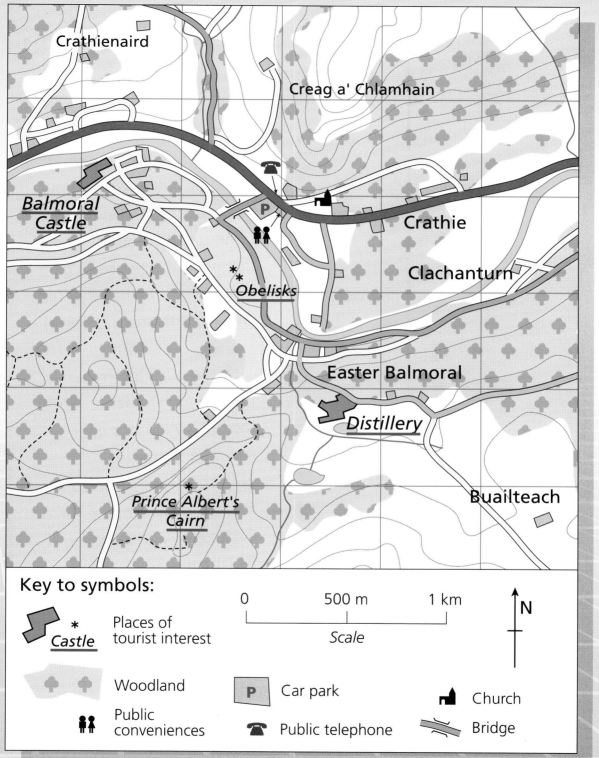

Crathienaird

Creag a' Chlamhain

Balmoral
Castle

Crathie

Clachanturn

* *
Obelisks

Easter Balmoral

Distillery

Buailteach

*
Prince Albert's
Cairn

Key to symbols:

Castle *	Places of tourist interest	
Woodland	P Car park	Church
Public conveniences	Public telephone	Bridge

0   500 m   1 km

Scale

N

Andy and the mystery lady are at the famous Crathie Church, where the royal family go to worship ...

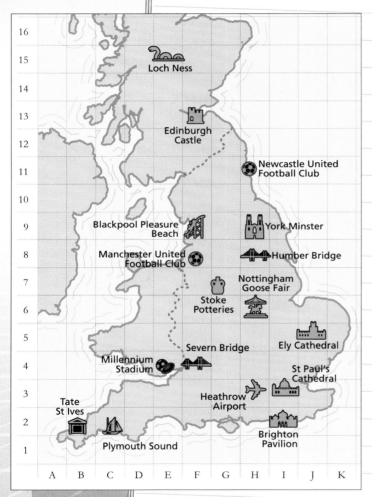

It turns out that the lady isn't You Know Who – it's Mrs Fraser coming to do some cleaning. Still, Andy's newsman's nose hasn't let him down ... he has sniffed out a great story anyway.

It turns out Mrs Fraser is no ordinary cleaner. She's the author of this year's surprise bestseller, *Nice and Clean – A Cleaner Visits Ten Nice English Places*. Crathie Church is going to be in her next book, *A Clean Sweep in Scotland*.

Which ten places in England did she visit? Find them in these grid references:

B2   E4   F8   H11   F13   E15   J5   G7   C2   H8

The answer is on page 31. ▶

Escape from the Evil Regent

Your father was the King of Kymuria, and your mother was the Queen. Now both your parents are dead. One day, as their only child, you will come to the throne, but at the moment you are too young. You are living in Black Crag Castle with your **guardian**, the magician Mazarin. He is teaching you all you will need to know when you are old enough to rule the country. In the meantime, your uncle is standing in for you, and ruling as **regent**.

But your uncle has developed a taste for power. He doesn't want to give it up. If you were to die, he would be King. He wants you dead ... and he is coming to get you!

The castle is surrounded by dangers. There is an acid bog to the north, and perilous peaks to the east. To the south is a deep, rushing river. The only road to the castle comes through thick forests. You don't know which direction leads to safety, but the magician Mazarin does. If you can follow his instructions, you will escape and be safe. If you get it wrong, you will die!

There is a secret way out of the castle through a tunnel under the north wall. The tunnel goes under the moat. It comes out near the bridge to Bonemelt Island in the acid bogs.

Don't go over the bridge. Take the track that goes up to your right, and follow it south along the top of the **crags**. You will come to a deep gully with a river in the bottom. Don't cross it. Follow the river in a south-westerly direction until you come to a bridge. This bridge will take you to safety.

Which bridge will you go over?

Go on to page 26 to see if you were right. ▶

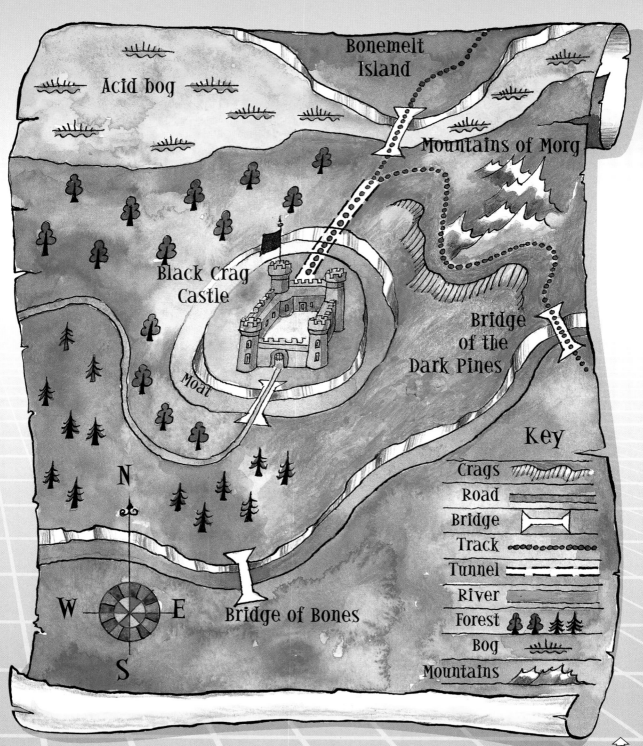

You have crossed the Bridge of Bones and reached the kingdom of Santora. You don't know this kingdom and will need a guide. Who can you trust — the King, the Garbolim or the Whaleman? Follow these directions and find out.

Go due east from the bridge until you come to some standing stones. Go south from the standing stones. When you get to the river, do not cross it. Follow it down to the sea, and go west along the shore.

Where have you ended up?

Check the answer on page 31. ▶

On the Trail of the Siberian Rubythroat

You are a keen birdwatcher. You live in Manchester, but you have travelled all over the UK looking for rare birds. You have heard that a Siberian Rubythroat has been seen in the north. Follow these directions to find out where.

Take the train from your nearest station at F1 to the station at G9. Go to the airport G9 and catch a plane to H14. Charter a small plane to take you to G13.

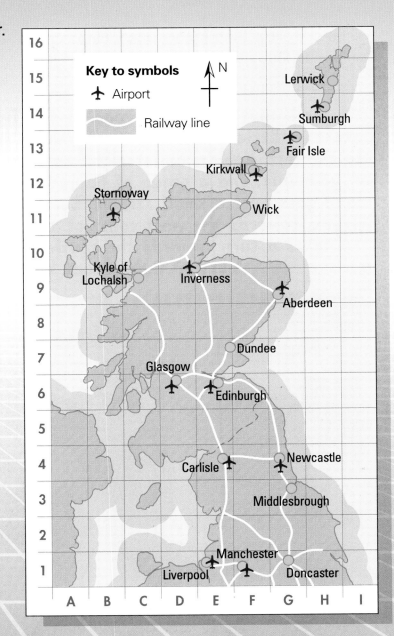

Where have you ended up?

Read on to find out! ▶

You have arrived on Fair Isle. Because of its position and the **prevailing winds**, Fair Isle has a lot of rare visitors, or **vagrants**, from the east. Start at the landing strip in the middle of the island. Follow the bird warden's directions to find the Siberian Rubythroat.

Walk south down the road to the **T-junction**, and turn right. A little way after the **TV mast**, you will see a turning to the left. Keep going straight on. You will pass some toilets on your left, and a group of houses. Just after the houses, the road goes over a small stream. Leave the road and follow the stream towards the west coast of the island. When the stream takes a turn towards the south, stop. That's where the Siberian Rubythroat has been seen.

Where are you?

Look at page 30 to see if you are in the right place. ▶

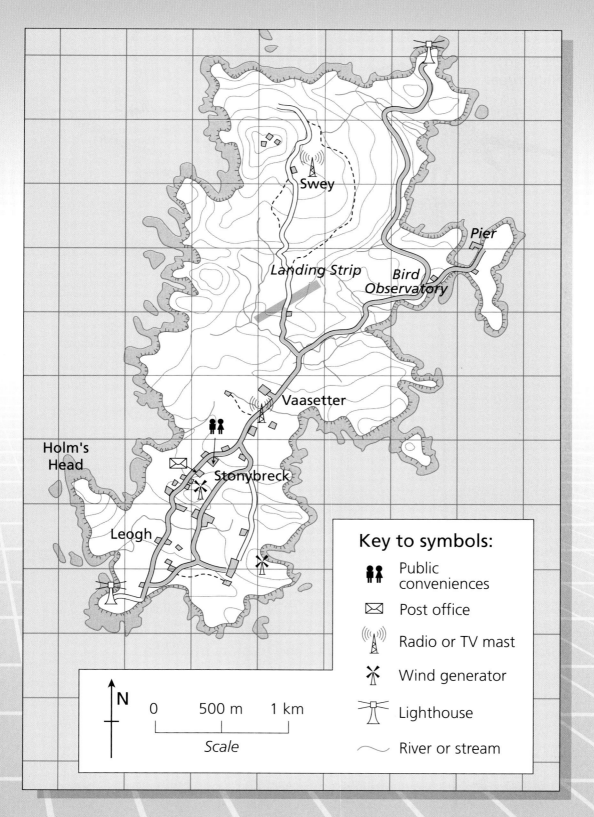

Swey

Pier

Landing Strip

Bird
Observatory

Vaasetter

Holm's
Head

Stonybreck

Leogh

Key to symbols:

👥 Public
conveniences

✉ Post office

📡 Radio or TV mast

✳ Wind generator

⛫ Lighthouse

〰 River or stream

N

0   500 m   1 km

Scale

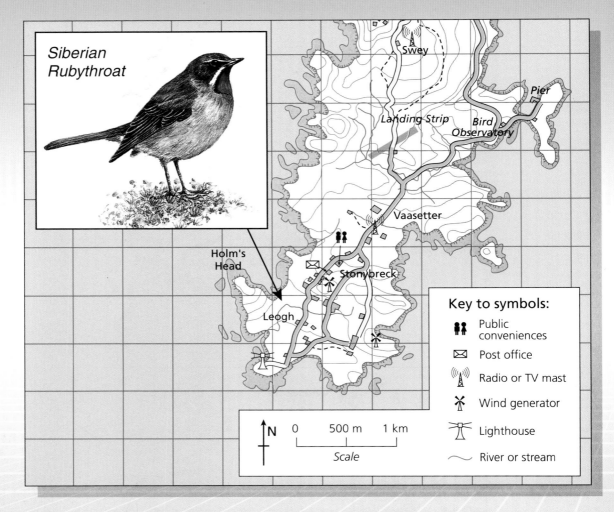

Siberian Rubythroat

Key to symbols:

👫 Public conveniences

✉ Post office

📡 Radio or TV mast

✳ Wind generator

⊤ Lighthouse

～ River or stream

↑N   0   500 m   1 km
            Scale

Are you in the right place? If so, you are amazingly lucky. The last time a Siberian Rubythroat was seen in Britain was in October 1975!

Now see if you can find the Pechora Pipit one of your fellow birdwatchers has seen. Go back to the landing strip and follow the track north. Almost straightaway, the track is met by a footpath to your right. Follow the footpath around the hill until you are due east of the radio mast.

Where are you?

Check the answers on page 31 to see if you have found the right place. ▶

Answers

Page 4

Leah's CD is in the vegetable patch, hidden among the carrots.

Page 8

Jan went to the toilets. Then she ordered a burger and chips. She went to the shop to buy a newspaper on her way out.

Page 10

Your dinner will be safe in the litebrite pool. You won't be able to see it because the bright light from the pool will dazzle you.

Page 18

The sweets are between the greetings cards and the jewellery.

Page 22

Tate St Ives, Millennium Stadium, Manchester United Football Club, Newcastle United Football Club, Edinburgh Castle, Loch Ness, Ely Cathedral, Stoke Potteries, Plymouth Sound, Humber Bridge.

Page 26

If you went to the Garbolim's cave, you got gobbled up. If you went to the castle, you were thrown in the dungeons by the King of Santora, who is your uncle's friend. The only guide you can trust is the Whaleman. He will carry you over the sea to safety.

Page 30

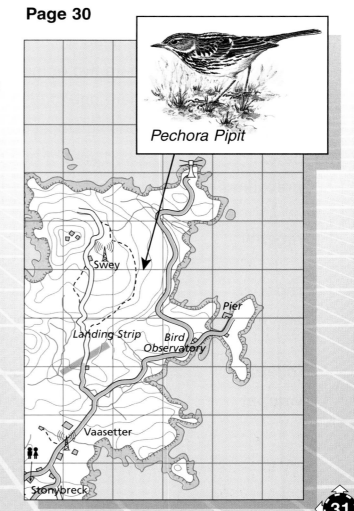

Pechora Pipit

Glossary

burglary — breaking into a building to steal things

cemetery — graveyard

compost bin — container for vegetable peelings and other plant waste, which will rot down to make manure for the garden

crags — steep rock faces like cliffs

distillery — factory where alcoholic drinks are made

drawing room — a room for comfortable sitting or entertaining

guardian — person who acts as a parent for a child whose parents are dead or cannot look after him or her

junction — where two or more roads join

T-junction — where one road meets another in the shape of a 'T'

obelisks — standing stones

patio — paved area of garden

prevailing winds — the most frequent direction of the wind in a particular place

regent — person who rules in the place of a monarch if the next in line is too ill or too young to take the throne

reporter — person who writes news stories

services — area close to a main road where you can find petrol, toilets, food and, often, overnight accommodation

toiletries — soap, shampoo, body spray, etc.

vagrant — a bird which is outside the places it normally lives